Guest Spot

Playalong for Flute
BIG FILM HITS

Wise Publications
part of The Music Sales Group

London / New York / Paris / Sydney / Copenhagen / Berlin / Madrid / Hong Kong / Tokyo

Guest Spot

Published by
Wise Publications
14-15 Berners Street, London W1T 3LJ, UK.

Exclusive Distributors:
Music Sales Limited
Distribution Centre, Newmarket Road,
Bury St Edmunds, Suffolk IP33 3YB, UK.
Music Sales Pty Limited
Units 3-4, 17 Willfox Street, Condell Park,
NSW 2200, Australia.

Order No. AM1010240
ISBN: 978-1-78305-874-7
This book © Copyright 2014 Wise Publications,
a division of Music Sales Limited.

Arrangements by Christopher Hussey.
Backing tracks by Jeremy Birchall & Christopher Hussey.
Flute played by Howard McGill.
Audio recorded, mixed and mastered by Jonas Persson & Imogen Hall.
Printed in the EU.

Your Guarantee of Quality:

As publishers, we strive to produce every book to
the highest commercial standards.

The music has been freshly engraved and the book has been
carefully designed to minimise awkward page turns and
to make playing from it a real pleasure.

Particular care has been given to specifying acid-free, neutral-sized
paper made from pulps which have not been elemental chlorine bleached.
This pulp is from farmed sustainable forests and was
produced with special regard for the environment.

Throughout, the printing and binding have been planned to
ensure a sturdy, attractive publication which should give years of enjoyment.

If your copy fails to meet our high standards,
please inform us and we will gladly replace it.

www.musicsales.com

All Of The Stars 6
from *The Fault In Our Stars*
(Sheeran/McDaid)
Sony/ATV Music Publishing (UK) Limited/Kobalt Music Publishing Limited.

Atlas 9
from *The Hunger Games: Catching Fire*
(Berryman/ Buckland/Champion/Martin)
Universal Music Publishing MGB Limited.

Do You Want To Build A Snowman? 12
from *Frozen*
(Lopez/Anderson)
Warner/Chappell Artemis Music Limited.

Everything Is AWESOME!!! 14
from *The LEGO® Movie*
(Bartholomew/Harriton/Patterson/Schafer/Samberg/Taccone)
Universal/MCA Music Limited/Kobalt Music Publishing Limited/
Copyright Control/Shawn Patterson/Lisa Harriton/Joshua Bartholomew.

Happy 16
from *Despicable Me 2*
(Williams)
EMI Music Publishing Limited/Universal/MCA Music Limited.

I See Fire 19
from *The Hobbit: The Desolation Of Smaug*
(Sheeran)
Sony/ATV Music Publishing (UK) Limited.

Once Upon A Dream 22
from *Maleficent*
(Fain/Lawrence)
Warner/Chappell Artemis Music Limited.

Skyfall 28
from *Skyfall*
(Adkins/Epworth)
EMI Music Publishing Limited/Universal Music Publishing Limited.

Suddenly 24
from *Les Misérables*
(Schönberg/Kretzmer/Boublil)
Warner/Chappell North America Limited.

A Thousand Years 26
from *Twilight: Breaking Dawn Part 1*
(Hodges/Perri)
EMI Music Publishing Limited/Fintage Publishing B.V./Warner/Chappell North America Limited.

Flute Fingering Chart 4

Flute Fingering Chart

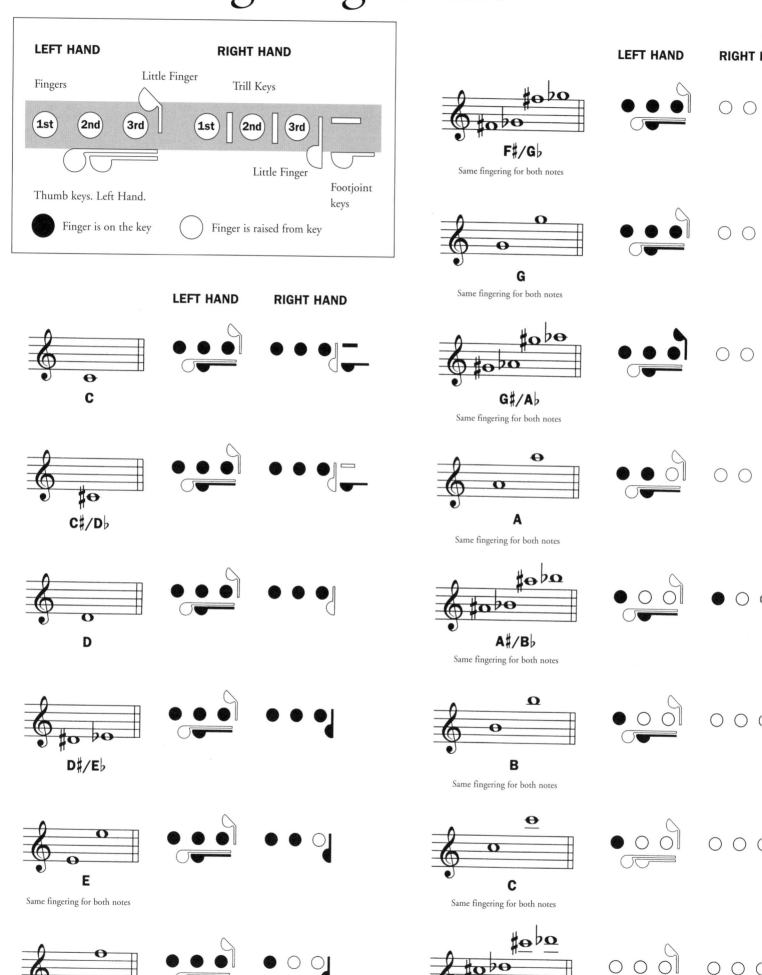

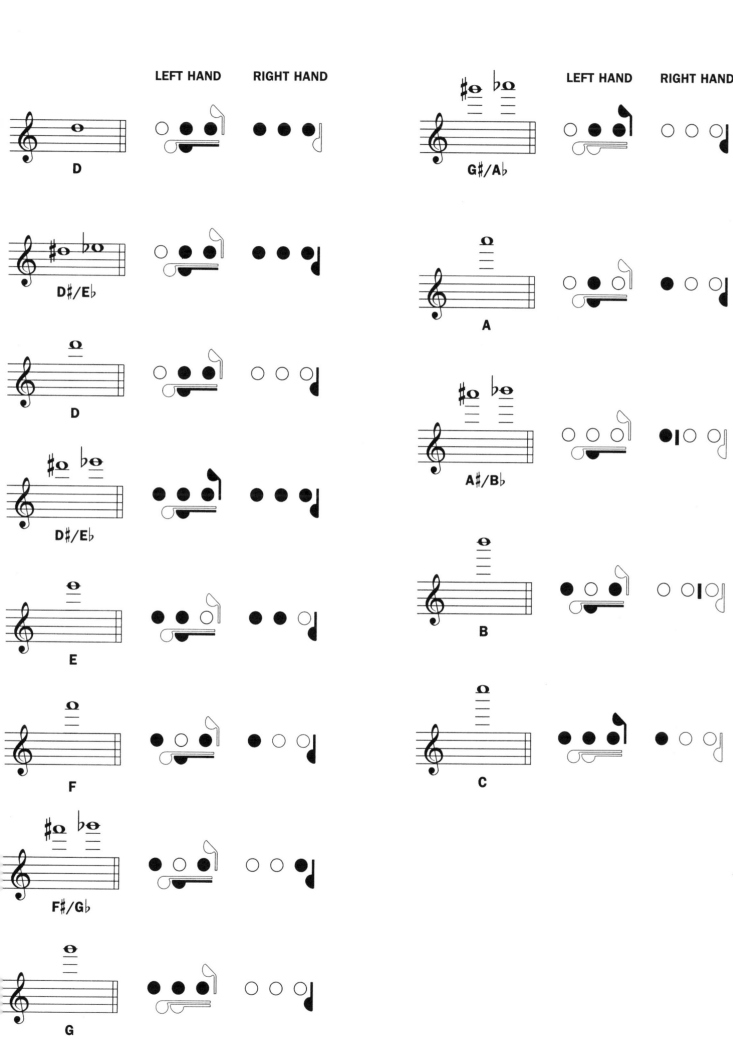

All Of The Stars (from 'The Fault In Our Stars')

Words & Music by Ed Sheeran & Johnny McDaid

Atlas (from 'The Hunger Games: Catching Fire')

Words & Music by Guy Berryman, Jonathan Buckland, William Champion & Christopher Martin

Do You Want To Build A Snowman?
(from 'Frozen')

Words & Music by Robert Lopez & Kristen Anderson

Everything Is AWESOME!!!
(from 'The LEGO® Movie')

Words by Joshua Bartholomew, Lisa Harriton, Shawn Patterson, Akiva Schafer, Andrew Samberg & Jorma Taccone
Music by Shawn Patterson, Akiva Schafer, Andrew Samberg & Jorma Taccone

Happy (from 'Despicable Me 2')

Words & Music by Pharrell Williams

I See Fire (from 'The Hobbit: The Desolation Of Smaug')

Words & Music by Ed Sheeran

19

Once Upon A Dream (from 'Maleficent')

Words & Music by Sammy Fain & Jack Lawrence

Suddenly (from 'Les Misérables')

Music by Claude-Michel Schönberg
Lyrics by Herbert Kretzmer and Alain Boublil

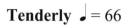

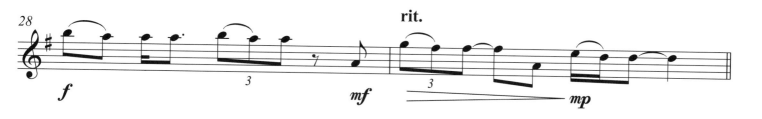

A Thousand Years
(from 'Twilight: Breaking Dawn Part 1')

Words & Music by David Hodges & Christina Perri

Skyfall (from 'Skyfall')

Words & Music by Adele Adkins & Paul Epworth

(brass cue)

HOW TO DOWNLOAD YOUR MUSIC TRACKS

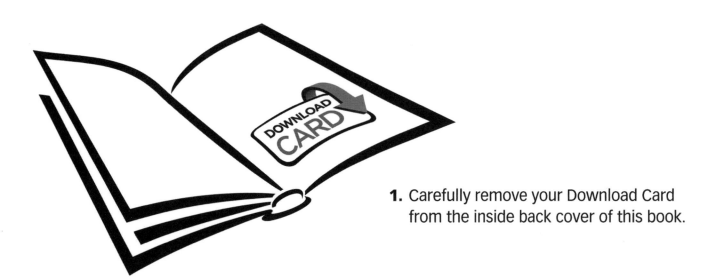

1. Carefully remove your Download Card from the inside back cover of this book.

On the back of the card is your unique access code. Enter this at www.musicsalesdownloads.com

TO REDEEM THIS CARD VISIT
www.musicsalesdownloads.com
ENTER ACCESS CODE:

XXXXXXXXXX

Download Cards are powered by Dropcards.
User must accept terms at dropcards.com/terms
which are adopted by The Music Sales Group.
Not redeemable for cash. Void where prohibited or restricted by law.

DCARD1006478

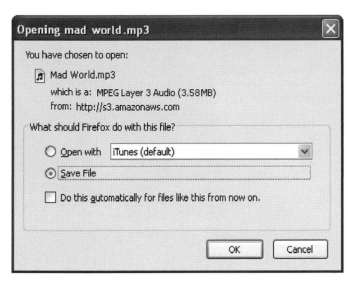

3. Follow the instructions to save your files to your computer*. That's it!

*Appearance of download manager will vary depending upon operating system and web browser.
In case of difficulty when downloading files, please contact dropcards.com/help
Card missing? Please contact music@musicsales.co.uk